Chill Out!

January
Build a snowman. If there isn't any snow, then make a scarecrow and stand him in the centre of your lawn.

February
Plant a tree. Not only is it good for the environment, but you can also watch it grow in the years to come.

March
Wait for a windy day, then try flying a kite. It's a lot more difficult than it looks.

April
Take up bird-watching and count how many different varieties of our feathered friends you can see in your garden.

May
Forget the maypole. Just get together with some mates and learn a new dance.

2008
Make it a year to remember.

June
Paint a picture. It doesn't matter whether it's a portrait or a view, do it in your own style and then hang it on the wall.

July
On the first of July, dig out a notebook and make a list of everything you want to do over the summer months.

August
Invent a new game - then invite some friends round and see if it works. If nothing else, you'll have a good laugh.

September
Dig out that list you made at the beginning of July, and see how many things you actually managed to do over the summer.

December
Write a book. Who knows, it could outsell *Harry Potter* and you could become a millionaire. If you do, please remember who gave you the idea!

October
Learn to play a [musi]cal instrument, [and] impress your [frien]d friends with [perfo]rmance of [Bo] Peep.

November
Look out all your shoes - and throw out any you haven't worn for the last six months.

4

What's In?

Some material may have been previously published.

Printed and published in Great Britain by D. C. THOMSON & CO., LTD., 185 Fleet Street, London EC4A 2HS. © D. C. THOMSON & CO., LTD., 2007
ISBN 978 1 84535 320 9

Dear, Deer!

Oh, Brother!

Carly loved her younger brother but there were times when she could happily swap him for a hedgehog. Like one day last year—

9

12

13

Two pages of seasonal puzzles with your pals from...

The Comp

The gang from Redvale can't wait to start their holiday and they've joined together to list all their favourite Christmas things. Can you find them hidden in this wordsquare? Words can read up, down, across or diagonally and letters can be used more than once. When you have found everything, the unused letters will spell out a message. What is it?

S	C	B	R	G	A	V	Y	G	P	E	D
T	R	E	A	R	N	E	N	A	Y	E	M
N	A	L	T	E	K	I	R	R	C	R	H
E	C	L	S	R	K	T	P	O	Y	O	C
S	K	S	U	C	I	C	R	P	L	H	R
E	E	T	O	E	I	A	A	L	O	S	L
R	R	T	S	T	T	M	Y	R	A	H	E
P	S	G	N	I	D	D	U	P	D	S	S
T	O	H	O	L	I	D	A	Y	S	S	N
Y	O	N	R	E	T	T	I	L	G	U	I
A	S	C	A	R	O	L	S	E	E	R	T
L	L	S	U	A	L	C	A	T	N	A	S

- BELLS
- CARDS
- CAROLS
- CRACKERS
- DECORATIONS
- GLITTER
- HOLIDAYS
- HOLLY
- PARTIES
- PRESENTS
- PUDDING
- SANTA CLAUS
- SHOPPING
- STAR
- STOCKING
- TINSEL
- TREE
- TURKEY

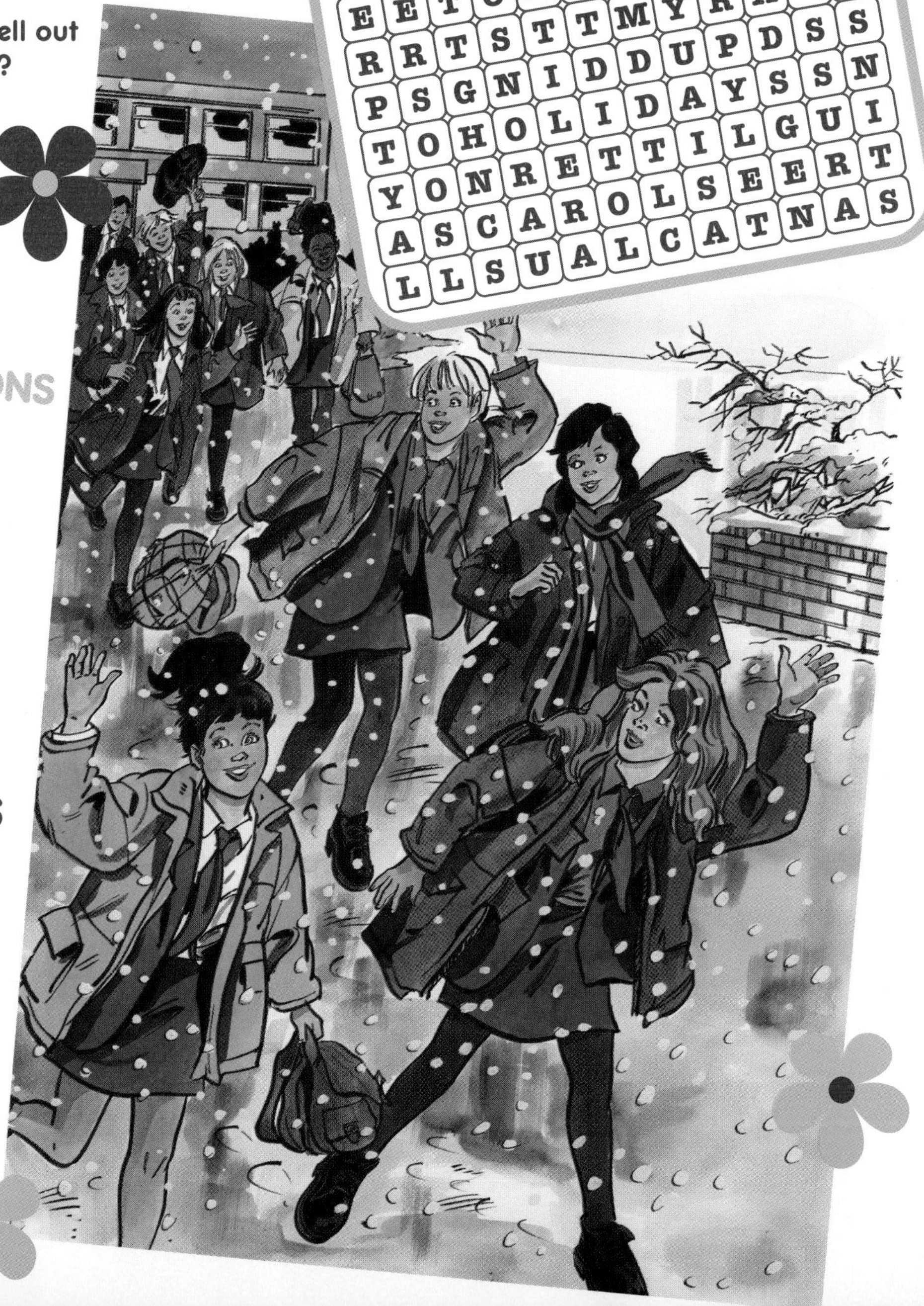

Laura and Becky have lost their way while out Christmas shopping. Make them smile by leading them through the maze and back to the shops again.

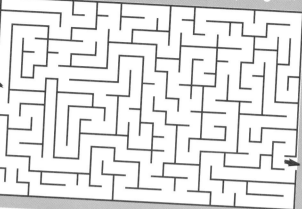

Later the two meet up with Nikki and Claire. Can you spot six differences between these two pictures?

Nikki has bought some musical socks. Unscramble the letters in the boxes to discover what gifts the others have bought. When you have solved the puzzle, the first letters will spell out an extra gift.

DIOAR

KOBSO

BRUELALM

RSAFC

NGAHDBA

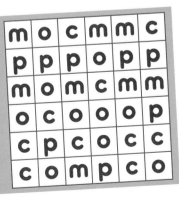

Just in case the girls forget the name of their school, the Head has set some special homework. How often does the word Comp appear in this mini square?

m	o	c	m	m	c
p	p	p	o	p	p
m	o	m	c	m	m
o	c	o	o	o	p
c	p	c	o	c	c
c	o	m	p	c	o

Answers

Hidden message A very merry Christmas to you all
Differences Snow on claire's jacket; 'U' from shop sign; Laura's trousers; Becky's scarf; Nikki's eyebrow missing; wood below window on bottom right missing.
Gifts Books, Radio, Umbrella, Scarf, Handbag. Extra gift Brush
Comp Square The word Comp appears seven times

15

Are You a Fabby Friend?

Find out with this fun flowchart.

MEGA-MATE
You stick up for her when she's in trouble, comfort her when she's sad and celebrate with her when she's happy. Your friend is a lucky lady indeed.

PERHAPS PAL
You are almost the perfect pal, but can spoil things by sometimes being a bit selfish or disloyal. Try to treat her with a bit more care and, in no time, you'll be a mega-mate, too!

SNEAKY SISTER
How would you like it if your friend was as sneaky with you as you are with her? A good friend is hard to find, so try being a bit kinder and you'll both be so much happier!

16

Meet Holly, Stephanie, Ruby W, Rachel, Ruby V and Hettie. The six girls are all great friends and couldn't wait to tell us all about ...

Their Favourite ✿ Things!

Raindrops on roses and whiskers on kittens don't rate all that highly with our crew - but that doesn't mean they have nothing to talk about. Oh, no! Chatting is cetainly a talent the girls all share - as you'll soon find out.

Describe your favourite outfit.
Stephanie: Jeans, black jumper and white, sparkly top.
Ruby W: It's a black dress with diamonds! (What, real ones?)
Rachel: A black and silver outfit with a puffball skirt.
Hettie: Jeans with a Von Dutch t-shirt and a purple blouse.
Holly: Green jumper, ra-ra skirt, chunky necklace and tights.
Ruby V: Black skirt, funky top, hoodie and footless tights.

Where do you most like to shop?
Holly: I like H & M, Topshop and Warehouse.
Stephanie: H & M, Topshop and New Look.
Ruby V: The same as Stephanie - oh, and I like going to Zara, too.
Ruby W: I've nothing to add to that. They're all great
Rachel: I agree.
Hettie: Me too - and loads more. I just love shopping.

If you could dress like someone famous, who would be your favourite?
Rachel: Christina Aguilera or Hilary Duff.
Hettie: That's hard. I'll have to think about it. (She then forgot all about it, so we'll never know the answer.)
Stephanie: Myleene Klass.

Holly: Yeah. Myleene has style.
Ruby V: So has Beyonce.
Ruby W: Yeah. I'd rather dress like her.

What's your favourite thing to cook?
Holly: Chocolate brownies - but I'm always having disasters.
Ruby V: I'm not all that good at cooking, but I'd like to learn how to make Yorkshire puddings without burning them.
Rachel: I like making pizzas and cakes. I once put hot chocolate in the microwave and it exploded - the chocolate, that is, not the microwave.
Ruby W: Anything with chocolate - like crispie cakes.
Hettie: I mostly make cakes - but I'm not very good at breaking eggs. I sometimes make a mess.
Stephanie: Nothing, really. I'm a bit of a cooking disaster.

17

What are your favourite sports?

Stephanie: I'm very sporty and I like swimming, hockey, netball, trampolining, cross-country running, athletics and loads more. I also watch tennis and swimming on TV.

Holly: Netball, hockey, tennis, shot put, swimming, dance and trampolining. I don't like watching sport, though - well, unless it's a World Cup or something.

Ruby V: Trampolining and gymnastics - but not cross-country running. I also like watching rugby. Jonny Wilkinson is my favourite player.

Ruby W: Netball, squash, tennis, badminton and hockey. My favourite footballer is Ronaldo.

Rachel: I like football and netball best.

Hettie: I like playing netball, hockey and tennis. And I love watching tennis on TV, too - especially when Maria Sharapova is playing.

What's your favourite thing at school lunch?

Ruby V: Yorkshire puddings. I love them.

Hettie: Spaghetti bolognese.

Stephanie: Ravioli. Mmm!

Ruby W: Steak pie and apple crumble.

Rachel: The salads.

Holly: Tuna and sweetcorn sandwiches.

If you could choose an ideal meal, what would it be?

Ruby V: Christmas dinner. I just love everything about it.

Ruby W: Me too. It's my favourite meal.

Hettie: My dad's shepherd's pie. It's yummy.

Stephanie: Spaghetti the way I had it when I was on holiday in Spain.

Holly: Loads of cheese, pasta and crisps - all mixed together.

Rachel: Christmas dinner with all the trimmings.

What about breakfast? What's your favourite food for first thing?

Stephanie: Toast and Weetabix.

Holly: Cereal and toast.

Ruby W: Bacon and eggs - or toast - or cereal.

Ruby V: Chocolate croissants.

Rachel: Toast and cereal.

Hettie: Toast - or chocolate Weetabix.

FAVE FACTS! Holly's favourite person is Jonny Wilkinson, the rugby player. She's kept this picture of him for years. She likes to eat Galaxy chocolate - and, for some reason, she doesn't like her feet.

FAVE FACTS! Stephanie loves chocolate - especially Kinder Bueno bars. The thing she likes least about herself is her nose, and the thing she likes best is her hair.

FAVE FACTS! Ruby W loves her mascara. Her favourite munchies include salt and vinegar crisps and Dairy Milk Bubbly bars. Ruby thinks it's really spooky that both she and Ruby V were almost called Alice.

Where did you spend your favourite holiday?

Holly: New York. Just because it was cool.

Ruby V: Venice. We went on a water taxi, which was a bit strange. I enjoyed it, though.

Ruby W: Majorca. While we were there we went on an aqua safari and got to walk under water - sort of. It was really good.

Stephanie: Florida. I loved it - especially the theme parks.

Rachel: Paris. I loved seeing all the famous places. And the shops were great, too.

Hettie: Hong Kong. It was so different from home.

Where would you most like to visit?

Ruby W: Majorca or Fiji.

Stephanie: Fiji.

Holly: Fiji.

Ruby V: An African Safari.

Hettie: New York. I'd like to see if it's anything like it seems when we see it on TV.

Rachel: I'd like to go on a skiing holiday.

What's your favourite thing to watch on TV?

Hettie: Coronation Street.

Rachel: Hollyoaks gets my vote.

Stephanie: I love Casualty.

Holly: I like Casualty, too. It's quite exciting at times.

Ruby V: Hollyoaks and Easties are my faves.

Ruby W: I prefer Little Britain and Corrie Orrie. (That's Coronation Street, to the rest of us.)

FAVE FACTS! When she was small, Ruby V was given a little toy lamb as a present. He's still her favourite thing. The strangest present she was ever given was a wig. Weird.

FAVE FACTS! Rachel is a good singer and her favourite film is Grease. She was given an iPod as a gift a couple of years back, but her favourite present of all time is her Fairy Ted. He's cuddly!

What's your all time favourite girl's name?

Ruby W: I think Daisy is a nice name.

Stephanie: Holly.

Holly: Stephanie - or Lola. That's a cool name.

Hettie: My favourite is Ellen. And I like Harry for a boy.

Rachel: Milly rocks. But I like Daisy, Ruby and Lola, too.

Ruby V: I like Lulu.

FAVE FACTS! Hettie's all-time favourite movie is Titanic. She loves it. Another favourite is her pair of 'H' shaped earrings, but the worst present she ever received was a pair of knickers!

FINALLY...

The girls all have different tastes in footwear. Can you guess which feet belong to which girl? Turn to pages 84/85 for the answer - and lots more puzzles with the girls.

And —

WOW! IT LOOKS FANTASTIC. A REAL OLD END-OF-PIER THEATRE. COOL.

AND WE HAVE OUR OWN GHOST, ASHLEY. WE CALL HER THE LAVENDER GIRL — BECAUSE PEOPLE WHO CLAIM TO HAVE SEEN HER SAY THERE IS ALWAYS A STRONG SMELL OF LAVENDER AROUND.

HAVE YOU EVER SEEN HER?

NO, BUT I HAVE SMELT THE LAVENDER.

WE THINK SHE'S A GIRL CALLED LIZZIE LONG WHO USED TO SELL LAVENDER IN THE THEATRE DURING THE EARLY 1900s. WHEN A NEW MANAGER CAME TO THE THEATRE, HE BANNED HER FROM COMING INSIDE.

OH, WHAT HAPPENED TO HER THEN?

WELL, SHE NEEDED THE MONEY, SO SHE USED TO CREEP SECRETLY INTO THE THEATRE THROUGH THE GALLERY WINDOW AND STILL SELL HER LAVENDER TO THE AUDIENCES.

ONE NIGHT SHE RAN INTO THE GALLERY AND THREW HERSELF OUT OF THE WINDOW. IT WAS A HIGH TIDE AND SHE DROWNED IN THE SEA. THERE WERE RUMOURS THAT SHE HAD BEEN PUSHED BY THE MANAGER'S SON, BUT NOTHING WAS EVER PROVED.

POOR LIZZIE. PERHAPS THAT'S WHY HER GHOST STILL HAUNTS THE THEATRE. SHE WANTS PEOPLE TO KNOW THE REAL REASON SHE DIED.

22

Ashley wandered about for a while. Then, in the stalls —

BUT I HAVE TO GET ON WITH SELLING TICKETS. PERHAPS YOU CAN HAVE A LOOK AROUND IF TOM, OUR THEATRE MANAGER, DOESN'T MIND.

OF COURSE I DON'T. JUST BE CAREFUL — AND DON'T GET IN ANYONE'S WAY. OH, AND DON'T GO INTO THE REHEARSAL ROOM UPSTAIRS. YOU'LL GET CHASED IF YOU DO.

THANKS, TOM. I WON'T BOTHER ANYONE.

OH, I — I CAN SMELL LAVENDER. AND IT'S REALLY STRONG. COULD — COULD IT BE THE GHOST?

NO, THERE'S NO ONE HERE EXCEPT THE CLEANER IN THE STALLS.

But —

THERE'S SOMEONE UP IN THE GALLERY! I'M SURE I SAW SOMETHING MOVE.

YOU OKAY, ASHLEY?

ER — YEAH. I — I JUST THOUGHT I SAW SOMEONE UP IN THE GALLERY.

IT WAS PROBABLY A LIGHTING TECHNICIAN. THE GALLERY'S BEEN CLOSED TO THE PUBLIC FOR YEARS, BUT THERE ARE STILL ONE OR TWO FOLLOW SPOTS AND OLD BITS OF LIGHTING EQUIPMENT UP THERE.

OH, I SEE. FOR A MOMENT I THOUGHT IT WAS A GHOST.

AND I'M STILL NOT SURE. IT WAS MORE OF A BLUR THAN A REAL, SOLID SHAPE. AND IT SEEMED TO DISAPPEAR INTO THE WALL.

GRAND THEATRE

BLACK ROOM

Soon it was Joanna's opening night —

YOU'D THINK ZAC WOULD BE PLEASED TO SEE HIS MUM'S PICTURE ON THE WALL, BUT ALL HE WANTS TO DO IS TALK TO HIS MATES ON HIS MOBILE.

And —

YOUR MUM'S GOOD, ISN'T SHE?

SUPPOSE SO. BUT THIS ISN'T MY SORT OF THING.

MISERY GUTS!

Then —

WOW! THAT SCENT OF LAVENDER HAS COME FROM NOWHERE. AND IT'S REALLY STRONG.

CAN YOU SMELL SOMTHING, ZAC?

NO.

24

HUH! HE'S CERTAINLY A MAN OF FEW WORDS WHEN IT COMES TO ME. BUT I CAN DEFINITELY SMELL LAVENDER. I WONDER IF THE GHOST IS UP IN THE GALLERY.

At the interval —

I'M GOING TO INVESTIGATE. I'LL LEAVE MR MISERY ALONE WITH HIS MOBILE.

Ashley found the old stairs to the gallery —

IT'S A BIT CREEPY HERE. BUT THE SMELL OF LAVENDER IS STRONGER THAN EVER.

GALLERY

NO ENTRY

TCH, IT'S LOCKED! I SHOULD HAVE KNOWN IT WOULD BE. OH, WHAT WAS THAT NOISE?

AAAH!

NORTH

ON WITH THE

LLISON & B

WHAT DO YOU THINK YOU'RE DOING HERE?

continued on page 39

Leader of the Pack!

Are you born to **lead** or destined to **follow**? Try our fun quiz and find out exactly what you're capable of.

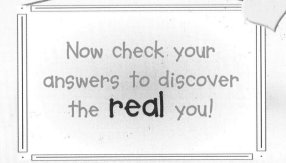

You and your friends are sitting around bored on a wet Sunday afternoon. Do you...

b) Laugh at your mate's idea of going to the park and suggest decorating jeans with stick-on fabric?

c) Say you're happy to go along with what everyone else is doing?

a) Produce the make-up bag and hair clips that you always carry with you, and organise a make-over session?

A neighbour has invited you to her birthday party and the only person you know there is her. Do you...

c) Try to join in all the party games. It's a good way of getting to know people?

b) Spend most of the party talking to your friend?

a) Bring along your box of conjuring tricks, and offer to do some?

It's everybody's first day at school and people don't really know each other. Do you...

a) Gather a group of people together and start swapping info?

c) Feel very shy, but try hard to talk to people?

b) Find one person who seems friendly and ask if she'd like to come to tea?

Now check your answers to discover the **real** you!

Mostly a

There's no doubt who's boss when you're around. Your parents were probably obeying your every command when you were in your pushchair, and it hasn't really changed since then. You've got bags of ideas, and you're great at thinking ahead – making you very popular. Just make sure you give others a chance to shine from time to time.

26

You're on holiday and have just gone out to the hotel swimming pool. Do you...
a) Take your own lilo, and invite other people to share it?
b) Admire another girl's water toys, and get chatting with her?
c) Sit quietly at the side and hope someone will invite you to join them?

At school your friend falls and scrapes her knee. Do you ...
c) Put your arm round her. Then ask her what she'd like you to do for her?
a) Take her to the loo and wash her knee. Then stick on a plaster?
b) Rush off and find a teacher to help?

Your local youth club is asking people to raise money to help keep it going. Do you...
c) Immediately hand over some of your pocket money?
b) Offer to help the organiser collect jumble for a jumble sale?
a) Get some friends together and organise a sponsored jog?

You're on a school coach outing and you're all getting bored. Do you...
a) Take out a mouth organ that you happen to have in your pocket, and suggest you lead everyone in a few songs?
b) Complain that people are singing out of tune, and suggest playing 'I Spy' instead?
c) Keep pretty quiet but join in with what most people like doing?

Mostly b

People may not immediately think of you as leader, but very often it's you who is pulling the strings. While you won't be the one to actually volunteer, you're probably the one who decides who *does* volunteer. Your friends really admire you, because you give so much support when they need it. And you always stand up for what you think is right.

Mostly c

Sometimes people may not really notice you all that much, because you're quiet and shy and seem to go along with what everyone else wants. But underneath you're a strong person and, in your quiet way, you very often get things to work out exactly the way you want.
You're popular with friends because you never embarrass them by making a fuss.

Famous Facts!

All the info on your favourite celebrities.

Mischa Anne Barton was born in Hammersmith, London, on January 24, 1986, so her star sign is Aquarius. When she was five she moved to New York City and she became an American citizen in 2006. Mischa is the middle of three sisters, with Zoe being older and Hania younger. Mischa attended the Professional Children's School in Manhattan and started acting at the age of nine. She is best known for playing Marissa Cooper in *The OC*, but other work includes the movies *Notting Hill* and *Lost and Delirious*.

Mischa Barton

Better known as Troy Bolton from *High School Musical*, Zac Efron first saw the light of day on October 18, 1987 in San Luis Obispo, California. Zac began acting at the age of eleven and TV work has included *ER* and *Firefly*. When *High School Musical* became successful, Zac, who has a brother called Dylan, had to change his phone number because fans kept calling him at all hours of the day. As well as acting, Zac plays piano and loves to take part in sport. His favourites include golf, skiing, snowboarding, rock climbing and surfing – which he took up while filming on the beach.

Zac Efron

Real Name: David McDonald
Born: Bathgate, West Lothian, Scotland
Date of Birth: 18.4.71
Height: 1.85m
Fact: David is the tenth actor to play *Dr Who*.
Other Roles: Barty Crouch Junior in *Harry Potter and the Goblet of Fire*

Name: Alex Pettyfer
Date of Birth: 10.4.90 in Stevenage
School: Shiplake College
Family: Younger half-brother, James
Facts: Alex, who doesn't like flying, loves skiing, diving and hockey.
Most famous role: Alex Rider in the movie *Stormbreaker*
Other work: Tom in TV adaptation of *Tom Brown's Schooldays*

David Tennant

Alex Pettyfer

Vanessa Anne Hudgens, who comes from Salinas in California, was born on December 14, 1988, making her a stylish Sagittarian. She is the older sister of Stella Hudgens, who also acts, and is part Filipino, Chinese and Spanish on her mother's side and Irish and Native American on her father's side. Vanessa's best known role so far is as Gabriella Montez in the smash hit movie *High School Musical*, but other work includes *Thirteen* and *Thunderbirds*. Dark-haired Vanessa got her big break when a friend had to back out of an audition for a commercial. Vanessa agreed to take her place – and the rest is history.

Vanessa Anne Hudgens

30

31

32

Lookin' Good!

No, this isn't about the latest fashion from your favourite shop, it's a peep at some of the hottest styles from the animal kingdom.

© J.M.Labat/ardea.com

Parrots

Parrots are famous for their ability to mimic human speech, but they have no need to copy anything when it comes to being attractive. Yellow, blue, red, orange, green – or any other colour you can imagine – parrots come in a multitude of colours. And while parrots look very attractive and colourful to humans, they look even more colourful to other parrots. This is because we see most colours as combinations of red, blue and yellow, while parrots see colours as a combination of red, blue, yellow and ultraviolet. So, when a parrot says, 'who's a pretty boy', he really means it.

Dogs

Everyone loves cute 'n' cuddly dogs with their hair flopping over their eyes – and many a girl has tried to copy the hair style. Mind you, it has its disadvantages for both dogs and humans, because it needs frequent brushing to stop it from becoming all matted and grungy. Still, the advantage for dogs is that the underside of their hair is waterproof, so the rain doesn't go right through to the skin. Pity that didn't work for humans. Other dogs we love include Dalmatians because – well, just because they're cool. And spots are sooo stylish.

35

Polar Bears

What colour is a polar bear? Believe it or not, they aren't really white – or grey or yellow. In actual fact these beautiful creatures have black skin which is covered with two layers of fur. The inner layer is thick and matted, while the outer coat is oily, hollow and translucent, and only appears white because of the light shining on it. These outer, guard hairs are rather wonderful because, being oily, they stop the inner coat from becoming soaked and, thanks to them being hollow, they help the bear to float. Now, that's what we call clever.

© M.Watson/ardea.com

Zebras

Zebras have beautiful black and white stripes which act as camouflage. That may seem odd because zebras hide in grass or scrub land – which isn't black *or* white – however, it works perfectly because their main predators, such as lions, are colour blind. The stripes also help to confuse another enemy – the blood-sucking tsetse fly. It's thought that the stripes send the flies cross-eyed and they then back off, leaving the zebra in peace. You could always try wearing black and white stripes to scare off anyone who annoys *you*.

© Ferrero-Labat/ardea.com

Goldfish

Despite their name, goldfish aren't always gold. They are a type of carp and can come in gold, yellow or several other colours. One reason why most are now gold goes back to ancient China, when it was fashionable to keep the fish in ponds. As yellow was seen as the colour of royalty, the Empress decreed that ordinary people couldn't breed any fish in that colour. As a result, gold became the most common colour and it remains so today. Personally, we think the Empress's loss was our gain!

Porcupines

© K.W.Fink/ardea.com

While many of the distinctive looks we see in the animal kingdom are designed to attract attention some, like the porcupine, are quite the opposite. These slow moving creatures are covered with up to 30,000 quills - which are ideal for discouraging unwanted attention. These quills are modified hairs of around 8 cm long with barbs on the end. If the porcupine is attacked he will lash out with his tail, hoping to hit his attacker. If he's successful, the quills will detach from the porcupine's body and become embedded in the attacker – which can be pretty sore. You could say that he's the original prickly character.

© J.Mason/ardea.com

Glow Worms

Female glow worms can shine a brilliant greenish light to attract males. They do this by causing a chemical reaction in the last few sections of their stomach, and they can turn the light off and on at will. Wow! As dusk falls the females 'light up' to attract the passing males. It's a bit like us taking a torch to a party and shining it at the boy we fancy most. But we'd never do that – would we?

© S.Hopkin/ardea.com

Peacocks

These birds are famed for their spectacular tail feathers which they fan out to attract the female peahens. These wonderful tail feathers are generally a mixture of blue and green and have 'eye' shapes all along the length of each feather. Like many birds, the male is more colourful and flamboyant than the female bird, but both birds have rather incredible head tufts – so the peahen isn't totally dull. In some parts of Asia peacocks are considered lucky, but in most of Europe it is considered very unlucky to bring the feathers inside. Personally, we think they look best on the birds, anyway.

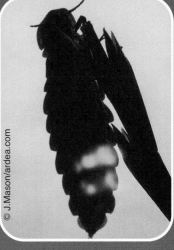

Bonnie Wright ♡♡

facts

Full name: Bonnie Kathleen Wright

Born: 17.2.91 in London

Also known as: Ginny Weasley in the Harry Potter movies

Fave actress: Nicole Kidman

Likes: Dancing, art, football and surfing

Fact: Bonnie plays piano and sings

So, next day —

IS IT OKAY IF I TAKE A LOOK AROUND THE THEATRE AGAIN, CONNIE?

OF COURSE, ASHLEY. AND ZAC'S GOING TO HELP TOM CLEAR OUT THE OLD STORE UNDER THE STAGE. I'LL GET YOU BOTH SOME LUNCH LATER.

IS THERE A PLAN OF THE THEATRE I COULD LOOK AT? IT'D HELP ME FIND MY WAY AROUND.

AND MAYBE I CAN FIND THE STAIRCASE I SAW IN MY DREAM.

THERE'S ONE THERE, LOVEY. ON THE WALL.

THE GRAND THEATRE

THANKS, CONNIE.

NOTHING EXCEPT THE STAIRCASE I WENT UP LAST NIGHT. BUT IT HAS TO BE SOMEWHERE, SO PERHAPS IT'S OUTSIDE.

And —

RAND THEATRE

THIS IS IT! THIS IS THE STAIRCASE I SAW IN MY DREAM. AND IT LOOKS AS IF IT PASSES THE GALLERY WINDOW.

NO ENTRY

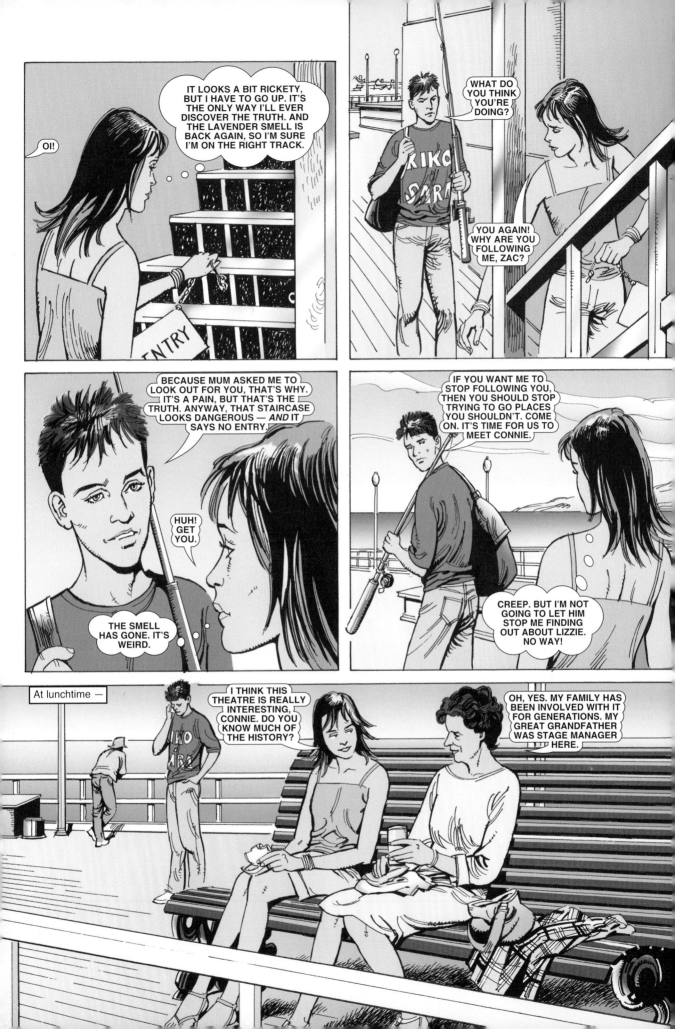

Then —

HEY, WHO'S THAT?

MAY I KEEP THIS? JUST FOR TONIGHT.

YES, OF COURSE.

THAT'S DONALD, THE THEATRE MANAGER'S SON. THERE WERE RUMOURS THAT HE PUSHED LIZZIE, YOU KNOW. BUT NOTHING WAS EVER PROVED. HE RAN AWAY SHORTLY AFTER THE ACCIDENT HAPPENED AND WAS NEVER HEARD OF AGAIN.

Later —

THE MORE I READ, THE MORE CONFUSED I GET. HOW CAN I FIND OUT THE TRUTH?

Then, as Ashley looked further in the book —

HERE'S A PICTURE OF LIZZIE — AND WOW! SHE LOOKS REALLY LIKE ME. AND — AND I DON'T BELIEVE IT. IT'S ONE HUNDRED YEARS TOMORROW SINCE SHE DIED.

I'LL FIND OUT WHAT REALLY HAPPENED TO YOU, LIZZIE. I DON'T KNOW HOW, BUT I'LL DO IT. I'M GOING BACK TO THE THEATRE IN THE MORNING AND I WON'T LEAVE UNTIL I KNOW THE TRUTH.

continued on page 67

What's The Job For You?

Are you cut out to be a **teacher**, a **vet**, a **nurse**, a **business woman** or **something else**? Try our fun quiz and see what the future might hold for you.

You want to earn some extra money, so which of these would you most like to do?
a) Babysit for a friend or relative.
b) Walk your neighbours' dogs.
c) Wash cars.
d) Ask for an advance on your pocket/birthday/Christmas money.

Which of these fancy dress costumes would you be most likely to choose?
c) A witch or a ghost.
a) An old lady or a punk.
d) You'd probably hire a complete costume.
b) A scarecrow. It would be easy to put together.

What was the main subject of the last book you read?
b) Animals or pets.
d) You can't remember.
a) Friendship or family.
c) Spooky things.

Pick your favourite food from the list below.
a) Pasta.
c) Chips.
d) Sausages.
b) Salad.

Which of these countries would you choose for a holiday?
b) Ireland or Scotland.
d) USA or Australia.
c) Romania or Bulgaria.
a) Spain or Portugal.

What would you rescue first in a disaster?
a) Your music collection.
b) Your pet.
c) Your photo albums.
d) Your DVD player and discs.

How do you like to spend Saturday afternoons?
d) Going to the cinema.
c) Doing something different every week.
b) Watching — or even playing — football.
a) Shopping with your friends.

How many of the following fresh fruits have you tasted? Mango, water melon, kiwi fruit, fig, paw-paw, star fruit, nectarine, coconut.
c) Seven or eight.
d) None, or one or two.
a) Five or six.
b) Three or four.

Conclusions

Mostly a
You're clearly a 'people person', so teaching or nursing would seem suitable careers for you. But if these jobs sound a bit ordinary, there are other things you could consider. How about a personal shopper or a party organiser? You like variety, so these fun jobs would suit you perfecly.

Mostly b
You're a caring person with a love of animals, so a vet or animal nurse would be your obvious choice of career. You're not afraid of hard work - and you love being outside - so if you're looking for something a bit more unusual and adventurous, you could try dog training - or even gardening.

Mostly c
Last week you probably wanted to be a manicurist, and this week you want to be a nurse. Next week you'll want to be a model - and so on and so on. Basically, you don't know what you want to do - but whatever it is it has to be fun and have lots of variety. An actress, travel rep or tour guide would suit you perfectly.

Mostly d
Organisation is what you like best, so you'd be great in business or banking. However, if you think flying off to meetings all over the world earning a fortune sounds too dull, then you could try starting up a housekeeping or decorating business. That way you could organise other people - and probably still make a fortune.

47

THE END

The Rainbow

by Tracy Joy Holroyd

"There's Carol. Why don't you speak to her?" Susan whispered. Sara stared across the schoolyard at her ex-best friend, Carol, noting how her face looked pale and pinched.

Carol looked back at her, lips thin, almond eyes large and beseeching.

"Why bother?" Sara replied coldly. "Last time I tried to make friends, she snubbed me. I can do without that."

"I can't understand you two," Susan shook her head. "You've been best friends for years but, since that stupid fall-out, you've slouched around like a pair of miseries. Everyone knows you want to make up again. Everyone except you two!"

It was true. Sara and Carol had always been close – then they'd had that silly argument. Sara couldn't even remember what it was about now, yet it had been enough to split her from her best mate. And that hurt – hurt more than Sara could tell.

But Sara had tried to speak to Carol only last week, and Carol had totally blanked her. Now all their friends were saying that Carol was sorry – and she certainly looked sorry. But Sara was determined to stand firm until Carol apologised. Then Sara could decide whether to be friends or to snub Carol as Carol had snubbed her. Show *her* what it felt like to be hurt.

"Forget it, Susan," Sara snapped, sticking her nose in the air as she turned away.

She tried hard to look as if she couldn't care less but, inside, she felt really miserable.

Saturday morning arrived and Sara still felt down. She leaned on her window-sill, watching the heavy, grey rain slashing her windows. It seemed to have been raining for weeks. She'd finished her homework - she was sick of her computer - there was nothing good on TV - she didn't feel like listening to music. Everything seemed dark and dreary. If only the weather would brighten up – maybe she could walk through the park or something. Sighing, she fell back on her bed and rolled over, closing her eyes.

A bright, cold light fell across her face, and she opened her eyes and squinted towards the window. The sky was still dull, but a single beam of silver light sliced its way through the cloud.

Sara crawled back across the bedcovers to the window. The sky looked magnificent - mountains of grey, trimmed with shining silver. As she watched, the light seemed to spread, growing and glowing like cold fire.

Sara's eyes widened as a huge rainbow suddenly appeared and arched across through the rain drops, and that the end usually moved just as you got close. But this time it seemed different. This time she was sure she would reach the end and find the treasure.

Dashing round a sharp corner, Sara skidded to a halt. It was magical. Light flooded over her – shining, crystal colours of gold, blue, violet and pink. For some seconds, she gazed up, entranced by the shifting lights, then she dropped her eyes and scanned the trees for the treasure.

When she saw it, her heart jolted, making her gasp.

Doors slammed at the back of the house.

"Sara? Is that you back?" Sara's mum shouted, glancing up from her film.

"Yes, Mum..." Sara couldn't wait to tell her mum. She could feel her cheeks burning with excitement and pure joy. She bounced into the living room and pointed to the door.

"Carol!" her mum gasped with surprise and delight as Carol, eyes sparkling, stepped into the room.

"I found Carol in the copse, searching for the treasure just like me." Sara gabbled.

"And we found it, didn't we?" Carol added shyly.

"So, what was it?" Sara's mum asked, full of curiosity. "What was this treasure, so special it has to be hidden in the magic of a rainbow?"

Sara looked at Carol then, reaching out, she grasped the other girl's hand.

"Why, a friend forever!" she replied.

the sky – the most wonderful rainbow she had ever seen.

Its colours were strong and vivid. They seemed to pulse with energy, glowing like some living thing against the slate-coloured clouds. And the rainbow was perfect – not faded or halved like others she'd seen. A perfect, full rainbow. And it seemed close. Very close. In fact, one end of the rainbow seemed to fall within a small group of trees at the far end of the field opposite her house.

Suddenly remembering the stories Carol had told her about treasure at the end of the rainbow, Sara leapt off her bed, slipped on her shoes and ran downstairs.

"I'm going across to the park," Sara explained hurriedly as she dashed through the living room. "There's a perfect rainbow and it ends just by the trees. I'm going to see if there really is treasure."

Mum laughed softly, but Sara didn't notice. She was through the door as if a pack of werewolves was chasing after her.

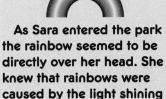

As Sara entered the park the rainbow seemed to be directly over her head. She knew that rainbows were caused by the light shining

Surprise!

ZOE GRANGER loved horses and spent all her free time at the local stables. One Saturday morning —

WELL, THAT'S THE MUCKING OUT DONE. NOW I CAN START GROOMING. THAT'S MUCH MORE FUN.

HI, ZOE. BUSY AS USUAL?

YEAH, SUZE. ENJOY YOUR RIDE?

SUZE AND FAY ARE DEAD LUCKY HAVING THEIR OWN PONIES. I WISH MUM AND DAD COULD AFFORD TO GET ME ONE.

The following week —

ZOE! CAN YOU COME OVER HERE FOR A MINUTE? I'VE SOMEONE I WANT YOU TO MEET.

SURE, JODIE.

THIS IS TEMPO. HE'S HERE WHILE HIS OWNER IS ABROAD. I'D LIKE YOU TO HELP HIM SETTLE IN.

BRILLIANT. HE'S GORGEOUS, JODIE.

YOU'RE A FRIENDLY BOY, AREN'T YOU, TEMPO. I THINK WE'RE GOING TO BE GREAT FRIENDS.

And —

STAND STILL, BOY. I'LL SOON BE FINISHED.

THAT'S HIM DONE, JODIE. HE REALLY SEEMED TO ENJOY BEING GROOMED.

AND YOU'VE DONE A GOOD JOB, ZOE. I THINK YOU SHOULD TAKE HIM OUT FOR A RIDE TOMORROW.

54

Fun! Fun! Fun!

Two pages packed with puzzles. Enjoy!

ALL MIXED UP!

The names of some of our favourite TV programmes and films have become mixed up. Can you sort them out?

wallace and who?

- Charlie and the **Goblet of Fire**
- Tom and **Gromit**
- Over the **Aliens**
- Pirates of the **Chocolate Factory**
- My Parents are **Away**
- Harry Potter and the **Hedge**
- Wallace and **Jerry**
- Home and **Vampire**
- Mona the **Caribbean**

TREASURE QUEST!

Which path leads Orlando and Keira to the pirate gold?

a   b   c

TV TROUBLE!

Unscramble the words to find some well-known TV programmes. What do they all have in common?

a) NEDTSERASE
b) NORAOTICNO ERTEST
c) YLOLAOKSH
d) REDMAMELE

WORD POWER!

How many words of three letters can you make from the word below?

TELEVISION

1-6	switched off
7-11	on standby
12-15	switched on
16 and over	channel queen

FIND THE LADIES!

Can you find the names of some of our favourite ladies hidden in this word square? Words can read up, down, backwards, forwards or diagonally - and letters can be used more than once. Happy searching!

- SUGABABES
- BILLIE PIPER
- KELLY CLARKSON
- ATOMIC KITTEN
- GIRLS ALOUD
- SHARON OSBOURNE
- KELLY OSBOURNE
- LEONA LEWIS
- KONNIE HUQ
- PARIS HILTON
- MADONNA
- BONNIE WRIGHT
- EMMA WATSON
- DANI HARMER

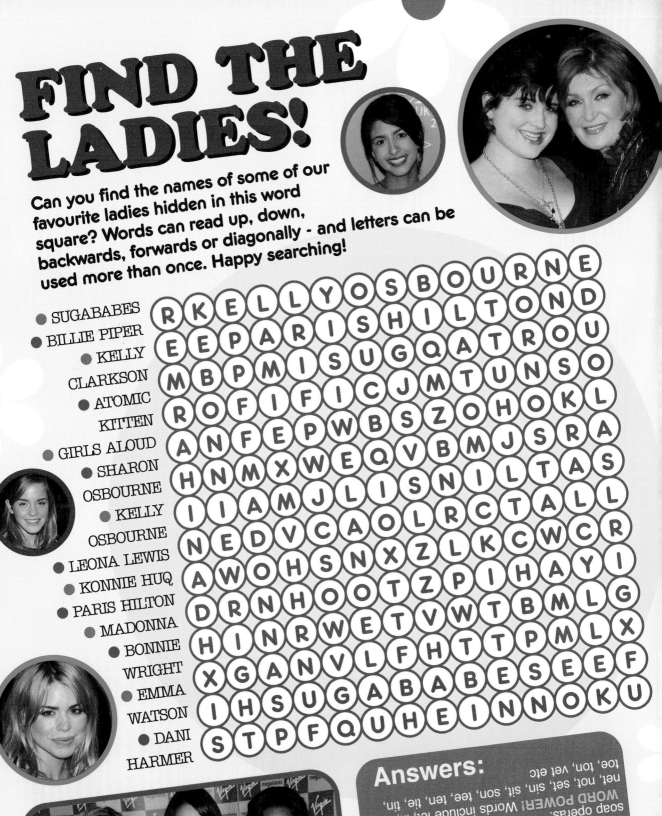

The word square letters read:

```
R K E L L Y O S B O U R N E E
E E P A R I S H I L T O N D
M B P M I S U G Q A T R O U
R O F I F I C J M T U N S O
A N F E P W B S Z O H O K L
H N M X W E Q V B M J S R A
I I A M J L I S N I L T A S
N E D V C A O L R C T A L L
A W O H S N X Z L K C W C R
D R N H O O T Z P I H A Y I
H I N R W E T V W T B M L G
X G A N V L F H T T P M L X
I H S U G A B A B E S E E F
S T P F Q U H E I N N O K U
```

58

At last —

THAT'S THE FIRE STARTED AT LAST. WE'LL SOON WARM UP.

THANK GOODNESS. MY EYES FEEL REALLY TIRED AND I . . .

Suddenly —

MEGAN! MEGAN! WAKE UP!

EH? WHAT?

TIME TO GET UP, MEGAN. AND LOOK. THE WEATHER FORECAST WAS RIGHT. IT'S SNOWED ALL NIGHT.

EH?

SO ALL THAT SHOVELLING WAS JUST A DREAM — OR A NIGHTMARE, MORE LIKE. PHEW! I'M GLAD ABOUT THAT.

BUT IT ALSO MEANS THAT I ONLY DREAMED THAT I HAD A DAY OFF SCHOOL! TCH! I BET THEY STAY OPEN.

But —

NO NEED TO RUSH, MEGAN. I'VE JUST HEARD THAT ALL SCHOOLS ARE CLOSED FOR TODAY.

OH! ER — DO YOU WANT ME TO CLEAR THE PATHS, DAD?

62

The Magic Garden

We all like looking at beautiful, well-tended gardens, but some people actually believe they are magical places and that many of the trees and plants have special meanings. Here are a few of our favourites.

An **OAK** tree has a gentle spirit. If you plant one in your garden you should be blessed with peace and shelter.

In the past, **HOLLY** trees were often planted because it was believed that they would protect the garden against evil spirits.

POPLAR or aspen trees are sometimes known as 'shiver trees' because of their trembling leaves. Long ago it was believed that witches grew them and used the leaves in flying spells.

Legend says that **IVY** growing on the wall of a house will protect the inhabitants from evil and bad luck.

Can you spot the fairies?

ROSEMARY was believed to have magical powers that could heal the sick. That aside, it smells nice, so it's always worth growing some in your garden.

The **FOXGLOVE** is said to be a special favourite of the fairies. Grow it if you want to please the little people! But don't touch it because it's poisonous.

* **Even the small animals and birds that visit our gardens may have come for more than just the food we leave out for them.**

A welcome guest at any time.

© P Van Gaalen/ardea.com

The sweet-singing BLACKBIRD was believed to be a good witch whose helpful and kindly magic made her welcome in any garden.

It's always lucky to see a **LADYBIRD** in your garden, and you should never chase it away. If one of the little creatures is accidentally killed, it should be buried gently in the garden. That way the luck will remain.

Lucky — and lovely!

© S Hopkin/ardea.com

The HEDGEHOG may look cute, but it is said that witches used to change into hedgehogs to disguise themselves. And how can you tell which is a real hedgehog and which is a witch? You can't, so best be really nice to the next hedgie that scuttles your way.

Can you tell which is witch?

Noisy little SPARROWS were seen as spirits of mischief - although they also brought fun.

When a ROBIN visits, he is said to bring gifts of joy and good luck, especially at the festive season.

Which mischief-maker started this squabble?

© D.Usher/ardea.com

© J.Daniels/ardea.com

FINALLY...

To make friends with your garden you must love everything in it and never harm anything – not even an insect! Weeds and unwanted plants mustn't be treated badly, either. They should be carefully removed and recycled in a compost tub. That way, they will stay a part of the garden.

Most importantly, you should take time to quietly admire the flowers, plants, trees and shrubs. If you feel tired or a little unwell, find a quite spot or wander round your garden and breathe in the scent of the flowers. It may sound a simple thing to do, but it's almost sure to make you feel better.

A festive friend in some festive foliage.

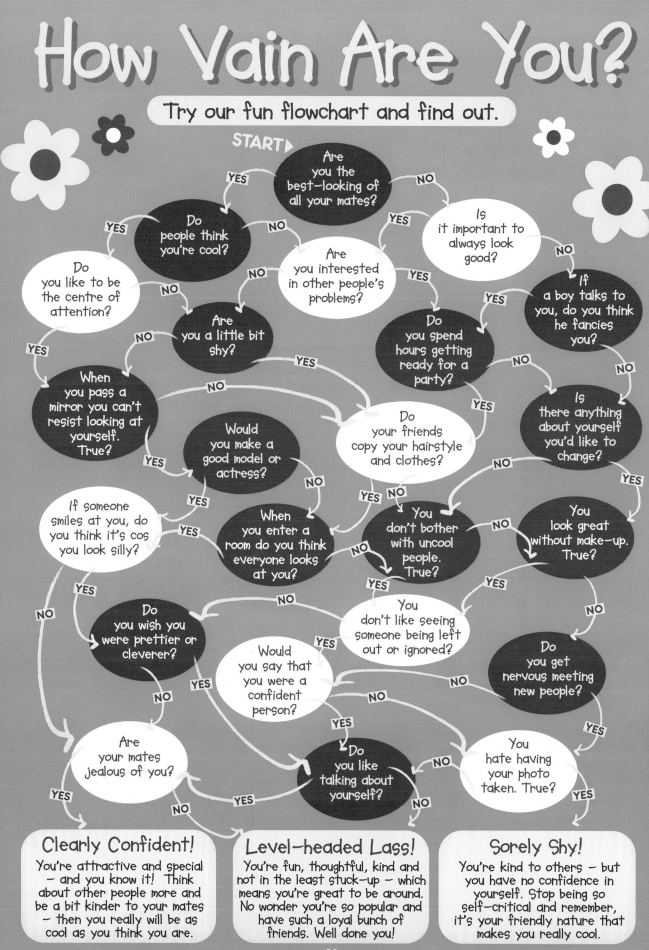

70

Curtain Up!

Working in a theatre may seem very glamorous, but that isn't always the case. As a young actress, ex-Bunty reader, Julia Eve, knew just how hard the work could be - but even she was surprised when she spent a summer season as Company Manager at Sidmouth Rep. She soon discovered that there is a lot more to putting on a play than just going on stage.

As Company Manager, Julia had overall responsibility for the day-to-day running of the company. Because the company performed a different play every week, this entailed changing the 'what's on' posters, keeping the cast photos up to date and other 'front-of-house' jobs such as checking the box-office returns and paying the wages. Back stage, Julia also had to consult with the set designer and stage managers and check that the on-stage set was exactly right before curtain up and that all costumes were ready and in the correct dressing rooms. Phew! Looking after the props when they weren't in use was Julia's responsibility, too - especially anything dangerous. These had to be kept locked away somewhere safe until they were needed.

Julia was also in charge of the programme for each play, which meant writing new copy and taking it to the printer in time for the opening performance each week. And, on top of that, she also appeared 'on stage'. Wow! Her summer season was certainly busy - but great fun!

Welcome to Sidmouth!

Time to open up for the day. Julia welcomes the public with a smile.

Cast photos are all in place. Julia's on the bottom row this week - but who knows what the future holds.

This week's programme needs a few last minute alterations.

Time to check the flats. It's hard to believe that these will build up into a set.

But they do!

Julia makes sure all the costumes are in the right place before curtain up.

Time for a little make-up before getting changed.

Julia plays a middle-aged doctor in this play - so her costume's hardly fashionable.

Phew! Another successful show. But there's no time to relax, cos it's curtain up again tomorrow...and tomorrow... and tomorrow...

73

The art Prize

by Susan Elizabeth Isaacs

S econd," said Daisy in amazement. "Second?" Her face darkened as she looked at the list of winners pinned up on the wall. Second was not a word Daisy was used to, particularly when it came to art competitions. She had won the top prize for her year for art, ever since she had started in reception class. Everyone knew she was the best. It was as simple as that.

Then a sudden thought hit her. If she had come second, then who had come first? Who on earth could have had the cheek to come top? Daisy peered short-sightedly at the list, and then put on her glasses. Selena Davis? It couldn't be. Selena was her best friend – and she had never seemed in the least bit interested in art. How could she possibly have won?

On Friday afternoon everyone crowded into the hall to look at the winning entries. Daisy had to admit that a lot of people had done some lovely things. But when she saw Selena's painting it was easily the best. A ballet dancer was standing at the bar, brown hair tied back off her face, one arm and one leg outstretched. Her reflection shone back at you from the mirror, and behind her a line of ballet dancers were following her movements. The drawing was superb, and the colours were beautifully done.

Daisy felt a twinge of jealousy. But then she swallowed her pride and went over to congratulate Selena. After all, she should feel proud that her friend was such a great artist.

It was when she got home that Daisy began to start wondering. Selena's painting was really lovely, but something about it reminded her of her favourite ballet stories. She had the boxed series on the bookshelf by her bed, and when she looked at the cover of the first one her mouth dropped open. It couldn't be – but it was. The dancer on the front page of her book was just like the one Selena had painted. Selena must have copied it. She had cheated.

Daisy didn't know what to do. Should she tell on Selena? After all, the competition rules said the paintings had to be your own work. It wasn't fair to copy and then get first prize.

Daisy had a bad night but, when she got up the next morning, she knew what she must do.

At break time, Daisy took Selena to one side and, nervously, held out the boxed set of ballet books, expecting her friend to look guilty or embarrassed. Instead, to Daisy's amazement, Selena beamed.

"Oh, wow, Daisy. I didn't know you had the whole set. Can I borrow them? I lost my box last year, and they're out of print now. When I was drawing I was desperately trying to remember those pictures, because I loved them so much. I've had them since I was six, and I used to go to bed staring at the pictures."

Daisy's mouth dropped open.

"You mean you drew your picture from memory?"

"Well, sort of," Selena blushed. "You see, Daisy, last

summer Mum sent me on an art course while she was working — and I loved it. The teacher's great and she showed me how to start by copying and then draw things from memory. I didn't say anything in case people thought I was just trying to copy you, but I've been going to the class once a week ever since."

"Can I see your sketches?" asked Daisy.

"They're not that good." Selena blushed again. "But the teacher keeps encouraging us, and showing us ways to improve."

"Not good!" Daisy gasped as she flicked through page after page of beautifully drawn ballet dancers.

"They're brilliant. When did you do these?"

"At the summer course there was a ballet class next door. They let us sit in and sketch them. But, Daisy, I'm so thrilled you've got those ballet books. It was the cover pictures that really made me want to paint and draw. Can I compare them with my painting?"

"Yeah!" Daisy smiled. "I'm dying to compare them, too."

❀ ❀ ❀

The two girls wandered back into the school and held the ballet book up beside Selena's painting. Now Daisy could see that there was no way it was a copy. Selena

had re-created the basic look of the cover, but the girl was really very different – and the colours and style were different, too.

"I'd love to be able to draw like you," sighed Daisy.

"But you've got your own natural style," said Selena. "You didn't need to be taught from scratch like I did. But you could come to my class, if you like. The teacher's fantastic."

"That'd be brilliant," said Daisy, her eyes glowing.

She might not have won the art competition this time, but she had a feeling she had won a far greater prize. A chance to make her future paintings better than she had ever dreamed possible.

The Twelve Days

Your cool countdown

✳ Day 1

Time to dig out the deccies, brush the spiders off the tree, and get things looking fun and festive - if you haven't done it already, that is. If your tree has already been up for weeks, then re-do the decorations.

✳ Day 2

Make up special messages to write in your cards. How about "If you're not careful with the holly, you'll end up sore instead of jolly"? Or "Santa's eaten too much jelly. Now he's grown a big, fat belly". Things like that. It's fun, fun, fun!

Day 3 ✳

Get out your piggy bank and see exactly how much you have to spend on pressies this year. If it's very little, then now's the time to work out ways of raising the cash. Offer to walk dogs, do shopping, clean cars - there's loads to choose from.

Day 4 ✳

The first step to shopping is to find some magazines and catalogues and look through them for inspiration. That way, when you actually go to the shops, you'll know exactly what you're looking for. That makes shopping much easier. Honestly!

✳ Day 5

Time to deliver your cards. Put on your trainers, warmest woollies, and hit the streets. It'll save you loads of money on stamps - leaving you more to spend on pressies.

✳ Day 6

It's time to look out all your glitter gear for the forthcoming festivities. You want to outshine the brightest baubles, after all. Remember, when it comes to glitter at Christmas parties, less is definitely NOT more. Go on, girl. Dazzle!

BEFORE Christmas

to the big day.

Day 7 ✱
You can't put it off any longer, it's pressie buying time. Arm yourself with a list and a bulging purse, and shop until you drop.

Day 8 ✱
Have a day of rest and pampering. You'll need it after all that shopping yesterday. Paint your nails (toes as well as fingers), soak in a bubble bath, give yourself a facial, or just chill out doing exactly what YOU want to do.

Day 9 ✱
Today's the day to sort out the pressies and get wrapping. Remember to decorate them with pretty ribbons and bows - the carrier bag they came in will NOT do - and make sure the cat doesn't try to help.

✱ Day 10
Luckily there's still time to hit the shops for those pressies you forgot. Or you could try making your own gifts. Things like home-made sweets always go down a treat with Grannies.

✱ Day 11
Take a trip to the local panto. They're great fun - especially if you join in with all the booing and hissing. Then join the carol singers and go round the doors singing for charity. A couple of choruses of "We Wish You A Merry Christmas..." should really get you in the mood.

✱ Day 12
Get up early and help Mum with all the cooking, cleaning, washing etc that needs to be done in preparation for the big day. Christmas at home is great - but it's loads of work, too. If you're going out for Christmas, then have a long lie and save your energy for...

...Christmas Day!

The Four Marys

IT was the end of term at St Elmo's School and some of the girls were already heading home for the Christmas break —

'BYE! HAPPY CHRISTMAS, EVERYONE!

HAVE A GREAT HOLIDAY.

SEE YOU NEXT TERM.

The Four Marys, Cotter, Radleigh, Field and Simpson, were staying behind for a few days —

IT'S GOOD THAT THERE'S A FEW OF US STAYING BEHIND THIS YEAR. LAST YEAR I WAS ON MY OWN UNTIL MUM AND DAD CAME HOME. IT WAS REALLY BORING.

WELL, YOU WON'T BE BORED THIS YEAR, RADDY, COS ALL FOUR OF US ARE HERE UNTIL THE TWENTY-THIRD.

IT'LL BE COOL. ST ELMO'S IS A GREAT PLACE — ESPECIALLY WHEN THERE ARE NO LESSONS.

YOU'RE RIGHT THERE, SIMPY. I WONDER IF WE'LL GET A WHITE CHRISTMAS THIS YEAR?

WE MIGHT, COTTY. COME AND LOOK.

YE-ES! I LOVE THE SNOW. COME ON, LET'S GET THE SLEDGES OUT.

79

81

WOW! LOOK AT THIS! THERE'S CHOCOLATE AND MINCE PIES — AS WELL AS LOTS OF BASIC STUFF. FANTASTIC!

MINCE PIES

MILK CHOCOLATES

And, that afternoon —

THE SNOW'S STOPPED AND THE ELECTRICITY'S BACK ON. IT'LL SOON BE LOVELY AND WARM.

EVERYTHING'S ALMOST BACK TO NORMAL.

And —

THE PHONE'S WORKING AGAIN, TOO, SO I CONTACTED THE HOSPITAL. ANDREA IS FINE, BUT THE BAD NEWS IS THAT THE SNOWPLOUGHS WON'T BE HERE FOR A FEW DAYS.

SO WE'RE MAROONED?

I THINK IT'S *GOOD* NEWS THAT WE CAN'T GET OUT JUST YET. WE'RE ALL TOGETHER AND SAFE. BESIDES, IT'LL BE GREAT SINGING CAROLS ROUND THE BIG TREE IN THE HALL.

DO YOU HEAR THAT, VERONICA? THOSE FOUR ARE SO CHEERFUL IT MAKE ME SICK.

On Christmas Day —

I THOUGHT WE'D BE OPENING OUR PRESENTS AT HOME — BUT THIS IS EVEN BETTER.

YEAH. THIS HAS CERTAINLY BEEN A YEAR TO REMEMBER. HAPPY CHRISTMAS, EVERYONE.

The End.

It's time to rejoin Holly, Stephanie, Rachel, Hettie and the two Rubys for some cool puzzles.

THEIR FAVOURITE FUN!

❀ FOOD FOR THOUGHT!

Rachel likes cooking. Unscramble the letters to find the names of some things she and her friends might like to make.

RIPCYS ACESK

LAHOCOECT WSRIBNEO

RIHMTSCAS NDRIEN

ZIPSAZ

RIHOYKSRE GDISUDPN

EPHRSEDHS IPE

SQUARE EYES!

The names of some of the girls' favourite movies and TV programmes are hidden here. Can you find them? Names can read up, down or across, and letters can be used more than once.

- CASUALTY
- GREASE
- EASTENDERS
- TITANIC
- LEGALLY BLONDE
- KEEPING MUM
- THE ITALIAN JOB
- THE HOLIDAY
- LITTLE BRITAIN

S	R	Y	A	D	I	L	O	H	E	H	T	C
Y	K	E	E	P	I	N	G	M	U	M	I	I
L	I	T	T	L	E	B	R	I	T	A	I	N
C	A	S	U	L	A	T	E	Z	H	Z	A	A
Q	E	S	C	A	S	U	A	L	T	Y	N	T
L	I	T	T	E	L	B	S	I	T	A	I	I
Z	X	S	R	E	D	N	E	T	S	A	E	T
B	O	J	N	A	I	L	A	T	I	E	H	T
L	E	G	A	L	L	Y	B	L	O	N	D	E

84

THE NAME GAME!

Starting in the top shaded circle, move up, down or across - but NOT diagonally - to trace the names of all six girls. Watch out, because there are a few tricky corners along the way.

STEPHANIE	RUBY V
HATTIE	RUBY W
RACHEL	HOLLY

```
R A C H P H
U R L E E A
B Y V S T N
R E I H E I
U B T O L L
W Y T A H Y
```

COLOUR CODED!

Solve the 'colourful' clues and fit the answers into the grid. When you have done it, rearrange the letters in the shaded squares to spell out the colour that all the girls said was their favourite.

- A black cat is said to be this.
- The coloured part of the eye.
- A small purple flower.
- What a red light means.
- A yellow fruit.

AND FINALLY...
Here's the answer to the little puzzle we set you on page 19.

Rachel loves her red 'Dorothy' shoes.

Ruby W's the girl in the brown boots.

Holly's Uggs are an essential part of her outfit.

Hettie sports her favourite pale blue trainers.

Stephanie adds sparkle with her silver shoes.

Ruby V likes to shine in her glittery pumps.

Best Friends!

This Bottlenose Dolphin and Risso's Dolphin get along swimmingly.

THE END